HQ

THE REAL GHOST BUSTERS

Welcome to the first ever fun-packed annual featuring **THE REAL GHOSTBUSTERS!** Those of you who have been following Marvel's **THE REAL GHOSTBUSTERS** comic every fortnight, will know to expect the unexpected, the unpredictable, the paranormal and the absurd in this all-new, 64-page volume. Those of you who haven't come across **THE REAL GHOSTBUSTERS** before are in for a real treat!

THE REAL GHOSTBUSTERS: dedicated professionals, sworn to the entrapment and containment of anything and everything that goes bump in the night. If you've got poltergeists partying in your pantry, or major demons manifesting in your master bedroom, ring Ghostbusters and rest assured — your ghost will soon be history!

CONTENTS

Noises in the Night!	5
Sarah Sangster's Spectre!	6
Ghostbusters – Busted!	10
Ghostbusters Fact File: **Peter Venkman**	17
The Spook from Outer Space! (Part One)	18
Ghostbusters Fact File: **Egon Spengler**	24
Jaws of the Beast!	25
Ghostbusters Fact File: **Ray Stantz**	33
The Spook from Outer Space! (Part Two)	34
The Return of Mr. Stay Puft (Sort of)!	40
Ghostbusters Fact File: **Winston Zeddmore**	47
Ghostbusters Fact File: **Janine Melnitz**	48
Office Bound!	49
The Real Ghostbusters: **What, Where, When, Why!**	52
Ghostbusters Fact File: **Slimer**	57
Spooked Out!	58

Cover by **Anthony Williams** and **John Burns**
Opening Spread by **Andy Lanning**, **David Harwood** and **John Burns**
Editor **Richard Starkings** Designer **Steve Cook**

THE REAL GHOSTBUSTERS™ ANNUAL 1989 is published by **MARVEL COMICS LTD.**, 23 Redan Place, London W2 4SA. **THE REAL GHOSTBUSTERS** title, logo design, characters, artwork and stories are copyright © 1984 Columbia Pictures Industries, Inc. and copyright © 1988 Columbia Pictures Television, a division of CPT Holdings, Inc. All rights reserved. All other material is copyright © 1988 Marvel Comics Ltd., a New World company. All rights reserved. No similarity between any of the names, characters, persons and/or institutions in this annual with any living, dead or undead person or institution is intended, and any such similarity which may exist is purely coincidental. Printed in Italy.

PETER VENKMAN

EGON SPENGLER

RAY STANTZ

WINSTON ZEDDMORE

JANINE MELNITZ

SLIMER

THE REAL GHOSTBUSTERS™

Story **RICHARD ALAN** ⊘ Art **BRIAN WILLIAMSON** and **TIM PERKINS** ⊘ Lettering **ZED** ⊘ Colouring **CHRIS MATTHEWS**

SARAH SANGSTER'S SPECTRE!

JANINE? ECTO-1 HERE. WE'RE AT THE *SANGSTER MANSION*, OFF *SANGSTER DRIVE*... WHAT'S OUR CALLER'S NAME AGAIN..?

JANINE TO ECTO-1... IT'S *SANGSTER*, YOU LARD-BRAINED MORON!

GEE, JANINE SOUNDS UPSET, *PETER*. I WONDER —

STOP WONDERING AND HIT THE *BRAKES*, RAY! OTHERWISE WE MAY HAVE *ANOTHER* UPSET WOMAN ON OUR HANDS!

MISS SANGSTER? *GHOSTBUSTERS* AT YOUR SERVICE! YOUR GHOST IS ALMOST *HISTORY*!

WELL I SURE HOPE SO! THE WRINKLED OLD BIDDY IS REALLY GETTING ME DOWN!

SCREEEE!

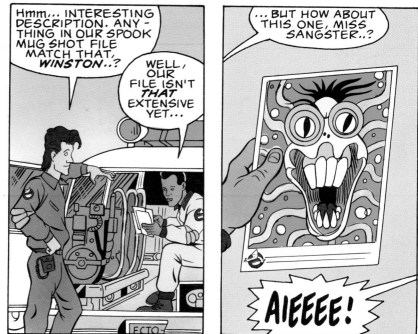

Hmm... INTERESTING DESCRIPTION. ANYTHING IN OUR SPOOK MUG SHOT FILE MATCH THAT, *WINSTON*..?

WELL, OUR FILE ISN'T *THAT* EXTENSIVE YET...

...BUT HOW ABOUT THIS ONE, MISS SANGSTER..?

AIEEEE!

Story **IAN RIMMER** ⊘ Art **ANDY LANNING** and **DAVE HARWOOD** ⊘ Lettering **ZED** ⊘ Colouring **HELEN STONE**

YEAH, NASTY LITTLE FELLA, ISN'T HE?

NO... NOT THE PICTURE...

...THAT!

WHO— ME?

EASY, MISS. THIS IS JUST *RAY*, MODELLING OUR LATEST PIECE OF EQUIPMENT...

IT'S A NATURAL SPECTRUM/ INFRA-RED PLASMA-SNAPPER INSTAMATIC...

...WHICH MEANS IT TAKES NEAT PHOTOS OF GHOSTS AND HUMANS TOGETHER— *SMILE!*

PHLK

HOW DARE YOU! I *HATE* HAVING MY PICTURE TAKEN...

HEY, DON'T *WORRY!* I'M SURE RAY GOT YOUR GOOD SIDE!

OKAY, TEAM, WE'VE GOT AN ANXIOUS CLIENT, A SPOOKY OLD HOUSE, PLENTY OF LIGHTNING...

LET'S *BUST GHOST!*

ECTO

INSIDE... DON'T FORGET – IT MIGHT *LOOK* LIKE AN INNOCENT OLD LADY, BUT IT IS, IN FACT, A SHE-DEVIL OF *EVIL!*

Hmm... PLENTY OF P.K.E.* AROUND.

*PSYCHO-KINETIC ENERGY.

KIND OF A *WEIRD* PLACE FOR A YOUNG GIRL TO BE LIVING IN, HEY, PETE?

YOU THINK *THIS* IS WEIRD? DID YOU SEE THE STATE OF *EGON'S* LAB BEFORE WE LEFT HIM THIS EVENING?

HOLD IT! DOWN THERE! LOOKS LIKE OUR GHOSTLY GRANNY!

PRIME YOUR PROTON GUNS, GUYS...

...Er, JUST ONE SECOND, WINSTON. THE PHOTO I TOOK OUTSIDE JUST DEVELOPED...

WHAT DO YOU THINK, PETER..?

WELL, IT'S GOOD OF WINSTON AND ME, BUT YOUNG SARAH SANGSTER ISN'T PHOTOGENIC AT ALL!

LEAVE THIS TO ME!

IS IT ALL OVER?

IT'S ABOUT TO BE...

8

YIIIIII!!

ZAM

YOU ALMOST HAD US FOOLED — BUT YOU'RE DEALING WITH *REAL* GHOSTBUSTERS!

SO IT'S *TRAP* TIME!

ZZK

UPSTAIRS...

SORRY WE SCARED YOU LIKE THAT, *MRS WATSON*...

Ohh... GOODNESS! WHEN I SAW YOU COMING FOR ME, I WAS TOO SHOCKED TO SPEAK!

LUCKILY, THE PHOTO WE TOOK EARLIER GAVE MISS SANGSTER'S GAME AWAY...

YES, SHE'S BEEN HAUNTING THIS PLACE EVER SINCE I BOUGHT IT. SHE'S BEEN TRYING TO FRIGHTEN ME OUT...

YEAH, SMART SPOOK...

CALLS *US* UP, ASSUMES HUMAN FORM AND NEARLY CONVINCES US THAT THE REAL HUMAN IS THE TARGET. OF COURSE, BEING *REAL* GHOSTBUSTERS, WE BUSTED THE *REAL* GHOST!

9

GHOSTBUSTERS

BUSTED!

Story **IAN RIMMER** ⊘ Art **ANTHONY WILLIAMS** and **TIM PERKINS** ⊘ Colouring **STUART PLACE**

Urrhnnn'. That was the sound. 'Urrhnnn . . .' a noise Spengler, Stantz and Zeddmore heard Venkman make twice in two days. This was unusual, as Venkman normally never uttered noises like 'Urrhnnn' at all. He'd more usually say things like, "What does W.A.K.O stand for anyway?" as he did when ECTO-1 pulled into the parking lot at the W.A.K.O TV station, the day before he said 'Urrhnnn' for the first time.

Nobody knew the answer to Venkman's question, not even the presenter of the station's best-known show, Johnny Vance. His programme, 'The Johnny Vance Show' was a live celebrity chat show which had once been popular, but was now sliding down the ratings. As a result, Vance was constantly making his show more and more controversial.

It was Vance who approached the four Ghostbusters as they climbed out of ECTO-1 to don their Proton Packs. "Glad you could make it fellas," he began, in a very smooth, charming manner. "Boy, do we *need* you. There's a plague of small, ugly, weird things running riot in the studios."

"Any previous manifestations of these alleged paranormal phenomena prior to your request for assistance?" asked Spengler.

"Er . . ." said Vance, glancing a little hopefully at the other Ghostbusters, his wide, presenter's smile fixed in place.

"He means," put in Venkman patiently, "have the little suckers ever shown up before?"

"Oh I see," Vance replied. "No, can't say they have. Of course, whenever things go wrong at a TV station for no explicable reason, we usually blame gremlins in the

system. But, er, it's not gremlins in the *system* we're worried about. It's gremlins in the studios, gremlins in the control rooms, gremlins in the toilets . . . in fact gremlins all over the darn place!"

"You just arrived for work this morning and the place was overrun . . .?" Stantz asked.

"In a nutshell," answered Vance, still flashing the required number of teeth for a TV celebrity. "But listen – would you guys object if we videoed the Ghostbusters in action for tonight's show, zapping these ugly critters?"

"Well, no . . ." said Venkman, straightening his Proton Pack. "I don't see any problem with that."

"Me neither," grinned Stantz with enthusiasm.

"Hey, why not?" shrugged Zeddmore. "After all, it's your TV station."

"Okay," agreed Spengler, "but

before any 'zapping' takes place we need to perform some tests, specifically for Psycho Kinetic Energy—"

"Arrh, *darn*," interrupted Vance. "The schedules for tonight's show are too tight. There wouldn't be time to video your tests, the bustings, and then edit it correctly. Maybe we'd better forget it . . ."

"Er, let's not be too hasty here!" answered Venkman.

The four Ghostbusters crashed through the doors of the studio brandishing their Proton Guns. They were closely followed by one of Vance's video crews.

"I don't like this," whispered Spengler. "We ought to run the proper tests before opening fire."

"You heard the man," hissed Venkman. "There isn't time for all that if we want to make tonight's show." As they advanced, Venkman spotted a mirror on a wall. "Besides..." he added, pausing to check his hair and teeth, "think of all the free publicity!"

"There's one!" yelled Stantz, pointing to a monitor desk. On it, a two-foot-tall, green-skinned ghoul with horns and a pointed tail sneered unpleasantly at them. "Eat proton ions, gruesome!" shouted Stantz, and he let fly a powerful stream of energy from his gun. The ray struck the ghoul square in its over-large mouth. There was a flash, a loud popping sound, and the creature vanished. Stantz steadied himself, turned to the camera crew and asked, "Was that okay?"

"Perfect!" came back Vance's voice from amongst a group of technicians. "Now go get the rest of 'em!"

So they did.

The four split up to different parts of the station, a cameraman trailing each of them. Stantz went to the offices and administration block. He pulled open a door and saw at least two dozen gremlins on top of

desks, chairs, typewriters and filing cabinets. "Okay," he thought to himself, glancing at his watch, "let's do this at the double." He sprinted forward, blasting his Proton Gun to left and right as he ran. Gremlins began flashing and popping to oblivion all over the place. He reached the far end, spun around in readiness to race back in the opposite direction, but saw all the gremlins had been zapped. He checked his watch. "Approximately twenty-five gremlins in . . . exactly eight seconds." He grinned in amazement. "Say, a new record!"

Zeddmore found himself amongst the various studio dressing rooms. He turned a corner into a corridor lined with photos of stars and celebrities – and gremlins. They were clinging to the walls in the spaces between the pictures. With great skill, Zeddmore blasted every single gremlin without letting his ion ray beam scorch any of the famous faces on the walls – expect one. That photo was of Johnny Vance himself, the beam burning away the grin from his face. "Hey

look," said a cameraman. "Winston's worked out how to stop Johnny smiling!

Spengler wandered towards a control room and was met by a horde of ghouls as he pushed open a door. He quickly closed it again, placed the barrel of his Proton Gun to the keyhole and pressed the trigger. The video crew recorded what happened through the control room windows, and loved it. Spengler remained unimpressed, however. For him it was easier than taking candy from a baby. "Perhaps," he thought, "a little too easy . . ."

Venkman went where he thought there'd be more cameras — the studio set. Instead, he found it just contained more gremlins. The set was largely in darkness, but the ghouls gave off a luminous glow, making them easy targets. Venkman got to work, firing here, there and everywhere, but always remembering to smile for the cameras. With ruthless efficiency he blasted all the gremlins from the set. When the last was ioned out of existence, Vance and the video crew burst into applause. A broad smile spread across Venkman's face, and he bowed grandly to left, right and centre.

Busting done, Vance saw them back to ECTO-1. But, as it pulled out of the parking lot, Vance smirked over to a technician beside him. "Okaaaay," he drawled, "let's go bust those reputations . . .!"

"Here it comes!" enthused Stantz as the Ghostbusters gathered in front of the TV set back at their fire station headquarters. Slimer, the pet spook they kept around the place, was also there, munching his way through a five-pound bag of popcorn which Zeddmore had bought him to keep him quiet. He guzzled away as a picture of the four Ghostbusters appeared on screen and Johnny Vance's voice filtered through.

"Tonight on 'The Johnny Vance Show' a sensational story! We expose this quartet of supposed heroes as nothing more than con-artists!"

"What!" gasped Stantz, Venkman and Zeddmore as one.

Spengler just stared at the screen, which now showed Vance himself. "Yes, ladies and gentlemen, W.A.K.O TV has exclusive footage that proves the so-called Ghostbusters are frauds. We had our special effects department rig up some simple spooks – and these 'ghost experts' couldn't even tell they weren't real . . .!"

"He cheated us!" protested Venkman.

"This isn't fair!" agreed Stantz. "He can't do this!"

"He's doing it," corrected Zeddmore.

"Burrp!" said Slimer, who had finished his popcorn.

Spengler never took his eyes off the screen, but quietly he whispered, "This is bad . . ."

It got worse. Vance tore into the Ghostbusters' past, claiming they'd caused extensive damage to public and private property with dangerous and unstable weapons. He left the clear impression that the ghosts the four had previously busted had been special effects they'd created themselves. He accused them of planting those effects in the homes of innocent people who then had to call the Ghostbusters to have them removed. By drumming up business in this way, Vance concluded, the Ghostbusters had swindled the public out of thousands of dollars.

It was all nonsense, of course, but even while the programme was still running, the calls started coming in from clients cancelling Ghostbuster appointments. Spengler made few more comments during the programme, but at the end he had a little more to add. "This is *very* bad . . ." he said.

Janine Melnitz, the Ghostbusters' receptionist/secretary, had to push through a small crowd of protestors that had gathered outside the fire station to make it to work the next morning. Zeddmore was busy at the switchboard, dealing with more job cancellations. The others were gathered gloomily around Janine's desk.

"Great show last night, guys," announced the straight-faced Janine. "You sure walked into *that* one with your eyes closed, your mouths open and your chins out, saying, 'Sock it to us, Johnny!'"

"Why did we have to employ such a smart-mouthed woman as our secretary?" asked Venkman, of no-one in particular.

"Go ahead, laugh it up, vapourbrain!" Janine sternly replied. "But let's see you laugh *this* off!" She thrust a newspaper under Venkman's nose. On it was a full-page ad for a company called Spectre Rejectors. The ad read:

"Competition!" said Stantz. "Cashing in on our current lack

of popularity!" said Spengler.

"Okay," said Venkman, "I'm a vapour-brain!"

When the hefty thumps landed on the door, the team were in the midst of a furious debate. Venkman, who was beginning to lose his temper, had suggested they take a live ghost from the containment unit in the basement and deposit it in the W.A.K.O TV station. Zeddmore commented that such a scheme went against all the Ghostbusters stood for. The thumps prevented further discussion and so Venkman went to discover their cause. Given his mood at the time, though, he was definitely the wrong man for the job.

He opened the door to see a large, thick-set, red nosed sergeant in a police uniform. More policemen were behind him, and beyond them was a small army of cameramen.

"Ghostbusters?" barked the sergeant.

"Could be ..." Venkman answered non-committally.

"You use Proton weapons?" the sergeant snarled.

"It depends ..." replied Venkman, again, giving nothing away.

"Lemme see the licence," growled the sergeant, completing his collection of canine voice inflections.

Venkman was genuinely puzzled. "The licence ... ?"

"Yeah, for the guns – let's see it!" barked, snarled, and growled the sergeant, all in the one sentence. He was enjoying this.

"Ha!" snorted Venkman, who wasn't enjoying it at all. "Let's see the licence for that stupid nose of yours!" The other Ghostbusters, who had gathered behind Venkman at the door, cringed visibly.

The hair on the back of the sergeant's neck bristled. "I can't arrest you for sarcasm," he said, "so it'll just have to be for fraud, trading under false pretences, illegal trading, illegal advertising, criminal damage to public property, criminal damage to private property – and failure to produce a Proton Gun licence!"

It was at that precise moment that Spengler, Stantz and Zeddmore heard Venkman say

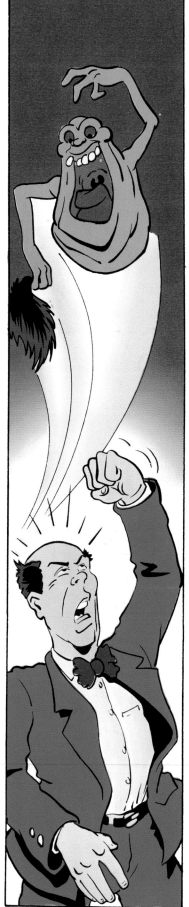

'Urrhnnn . . .' for the very first time.

The police took the Busters, and Janine, downtown for questioning. Yet only when he was certain that the place was empty did Slimer pass through the basement ceiling to materialise in the reception area. He'd heard and seen everything, and knew his ghostbusting friends were in serious trouble. He spotted Janine's newspaper and looked at the 'Spectre Rejectors' ad. Then he rolled the paper into a ball and tossed it into his mouth. Slimer has sampled just about all the world has to offer, yet he'd never known newspaper to leave such an unpleasant taste in his mouth as this. Something was wrong, and Slimer knew only he was left to put it right.

Slimer materialised at the W.A.K.O TV station in the middle of rehearsals for that evening's 'Johnny Vance Show'. The programme was planned as a phone-in, and the subject under discussion was the previous night's exposé. Slimer immediately began misbehaving, spooking technicians, tampering with equipment, swallowing a telephone or two and so on. His favourite trick, which amused the studio staff as much as himself, was to fade to invisible, sneak up behind Vance, then lift up the presenter's hairpiece. It seemed no-one, up until then, had suspected that Vance wore a wig.

Every attempt was made to rid the studio of Slimer, but all failed. An hour before the show was due on air, though, Slimer ceased tormenting everyone and vanished. By then, Vance had been reduced to a shadow of the cool, smooth TV journalist who had savaged the Ghostbusters' reputations the previous evening. But Slimer wasn't finished yet...

The show began, and a nervously grinning Vance took the first call. A husky voice came through, saying, "Call Spectre Rejectors to get rid of the spook behind you!" Vance spun around, and there was Slimer pulling faces at him. A second later, he vanished, just as another call came on air. A different voice was on the line, but

it said exactly the same thing. Once more, Slimer was there when the now gibbering Vance turned to look again.

It was Slimer who was responsible for the phone calls. He'd had words with his cousins, the *real* gremlins in the system, who agreed to provide the voices. On it went, until the studio audience took up the call for Spectre Rejectors.

Reluctantly, Vance agreed, and during a commercial break, the Spectre Rejectors were called. They arrived minutes later – two men dressed in bright red outfits, with large, visored helmets on their heads. They pulled a long cylinder on wheels behind them, which had two flexible pipes attached at one end. Slimer guessed that this was their busting equipment. Vance yelled something into the ear of one of them, then both Rejectors turned their flexible pipes towards Slimer.

But Slimer had spent lots of time hanging around *Real* Ghostbusters, and he'd learnt how to keep clear of trapping equipment. He was able to dodge and materialise all over the studio, always keeping one step ahead of the Spectre Rejectors. Slimer even had time to snatch Vance's wig and toss it down his throat – in full view of a camera which flashed the scene to millions of homes.

Eventually, Slimer completely exhausted the Spectre Rejectors who were forced, *on camera*, to admit defeat just as the programme ended. When the audience began to leave, the now shiny-domed Vance grabbed the Spectre Rejector he'd spoken to earlier and hauled him to the far side of the studio. Slimer vanished but followed them, secretly turning a video camera and mike on to record their heated exchanges.

"You red-suited baffoons," fumed Vance. "I thought you could bust spooks!"

"We can!" protested the Spectre Rejector. "Our equipment really *does* work. We just couldn't catch this one, that's all!"

"It's *not* all, you idiot!" Vance roared. "The whole country saw you fail, *live* on TV. They saw some weird, big-mouthed ghoul make

complete fools of you – *and* me! Don't you realise, I've put my life's savings into your organisation? That's why I engineered that show last night to discredit the Ghostbusters. With *them* out of the way, we'd have *cornered* the spook-shooting market – but you've *blown* it now!"

Their argument raged on, but Slimer had heard enough. He switched off the video and removed the tape.

Next morning, the first face the Ghostbusters saw through the bars of their cell belonged to the Mayor. "It seems the City owes you a full and public apology," he began, as the cell door was unlocked. The Busters looked to each other with various expressions of surprise then Venkman made as if to speak. Zeddmore, suddenly anxious, quickly clamped a hand over Venkman's mouth.

The Mayor, on seeing this, decided to continue. "A video tape

mysteriously appeared on my desk this morning. When I played it – after cleaning off all the green gooey stuff first, – it proved *conclusively* that you were innocent of all the charges brought against you..." He'd said enough for the Ghostbusters to realise who they had to thank.

Later, back at the fire station, Slimer came rushing to greet them after their release. He hurtled at them with his arms spread wide, and his huge mouth and tongue flapping in the air. Spengler, Stantz and Zeddmore dodged, ducked and stepped aside as their ecto-plasmic friend zoomed forward. Venkman was behind them, and didn't see Slimer until it was too late. They collided spectacularly and Venkman was left dripping from the biggest sliming he'd ever experienced. It was at this point that Spengler, Stantz and Zeddmore heard Venkman go, 'Urrhnnn...' for the second time.

URRHNNN...

PETER VENKMAN

Although Doctor Peter Venkman may often seem like the most reluctant member of the Ghostbusters, he is actually one of the keenest. He's a bit of a con-man and prefers to avoid dangerous ghostbusting situations if it's at all possible. Peter has a special affection for food, and all too often this brings him into conflict with the Ghostbusters' resident spook, Slimer. However, when the chips are down, Peter stops larking around and he's the one who takes the first steps toward confronting unknown menaces or troublesome spooks. When things go wrong, and sharp wits and fast-talking are called for, Peter Venkman is your man. If you were to think of the Ghostbusters as being one body, Peter would be the mouth.

The SPOOK from OUTER SPACE!

PART ONE

Story IAN RIMMER ⊘ Art PHIL GASCOINE and DAVE HINE ⊘ Lettering GORDON ROBSON ⊘ Colouring STUART PLACE

19

20

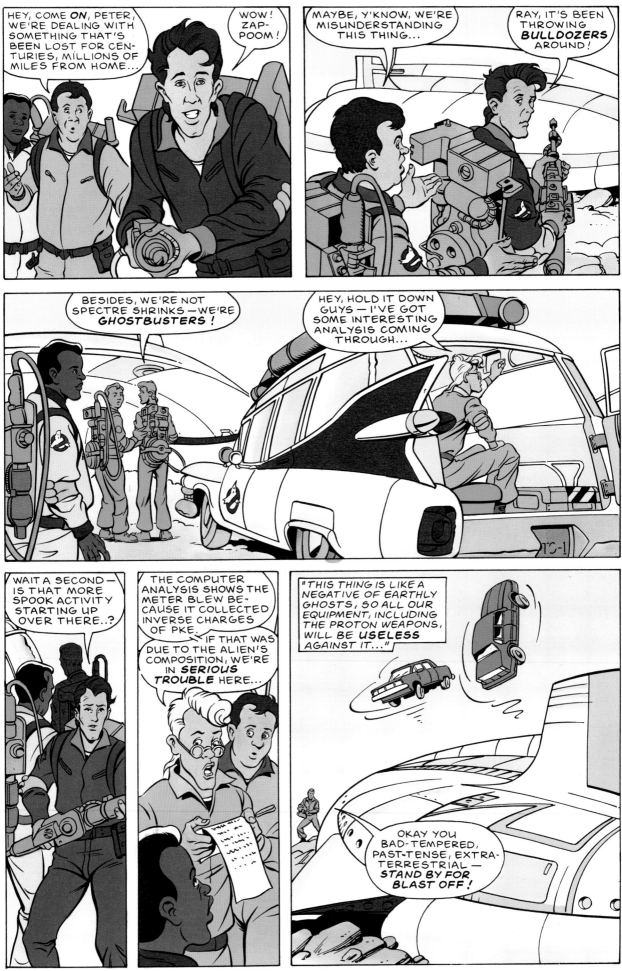

EGON SPENGLER

Described by some as a 'New Wave Mr Spock', Egon Spengler is something of an eccentric and has dedicated his life to the study of the paranormal – almost to the total exclusion of anything else. His sole hobby consists of collecting spores, moulds and fungus. When he's wrapped up in a problem, he is oblivious to anything else – up to, and including, the end of the world! He does have a soft spot for Janine, the Ghostbusters' receptionist, but he lives in a world that is very much his own – a place filled with equations, strange inventions and heaven-knows-what – and he has little time for romance. It was Egon who designed and developed the special ecto-containment equipment which helped the Ghostbusters become such a success. Whenever a problem requires the invention of a new device, Egon's the one to whom the task falls. In the body Ghostbuster, Egon would be the brains.

The merciless sun beat down on the primeval plain. Billy stood in the glade between the pine trees as the Tyrannosaurus bore down on him, huge jaws open, razor-sharp teeth glistening, breath smelling like a butcher's shop – This was truly the king of this ancient world. Billy shut his eyes against the Saurian's hypnotic gaze and waited in terror as the Tyrannosaur closed in for the kill...

Story **NICK ABADZIS** and **STEVE WHITE** ⊘ Art **ANTHONY LARCOMBE** ⊘ Colouring **STEVE WHITE**

JAWS OF THE BEAST!

Billy Collins' eyes snapped open and he lay in bed listening to his own breathing. It had only been a dream, but *what* a dream! It had all seemed so real, if only dinosaurs were around today, life would be so much more interesting! Billy sighed and remembered what the man at the museum had told him. He'd stood by the side of the ancient fossilised bones of the Tyrannosaurus for a full ten minutes before he'd been aware of the old curator's gaze. How long was it that the old man had said dinosaurs had been extinct? Sixty-five million years, wasn't it? Ha! No chance of ever seeing one alive now.

"But you'd *like* to see one, wouldn't you?" rasped a strange, evil voice from the dark. With a start, Billy lurched up in bed, about to flick on his bedside lamp. He stopped stock still when he saw the pair of glistening red eyes, hovering in the coal blackness of his bedroom, floating at the end of his bed – two red eyes, almost like the Tyrannosaurus in his dream!

Billy's curiosity soon overcame his fear, and he whispered, "Who are you?" The thing made a low gurgling sound, like water being let out of a bath.

"That does not matter," it rattled. "All you need know is that I have waited a very long time to speak with you, Billy. Together we can recreate the dynasty of the dinosaurs… Their glory, their strength… their elemental *power*!" As his eyes became accustomed to the darkness, Billy could make out a small hunched-over figure, almost like a tiny, shrivelled dinosaur itself. It gesticulated as it spoke, its red eyes weaving a strange pattern in the air, two leathery wing-like protuberances on its back rustling in time to its creaking voice.

"Would it not be wonderful," said the creature, "to bring the Tyrannosaurus to life once more? I know how we can do it."

At once Billy's blood rushed and he could see the Tyrannosaurus from his dream once more. Then the image in his mind faded and was replaced by the old, fossilised creature in the New York Natural History museum.

"How can we do it?" asked Billy.

"Go to your aunt's library," rasped the creature. "Take down the spellbook on the third shelf and tear out page four thousand and forty-three…"

A faint sense of guilt nagged at Billy as he took down the massive old book, the strange creature hissing with pleasure at his side. His Aunt Lavinia was a strange woman, renowned locally as a witch. Other kids kept well away from Billy because of it. Even in New York it was considered odd to be the nephew of a kooky old woman who kept dusty old books on great shelves and claimed she could speak to the spirit world.

Indeed, up until the appearance of his new red-eyed little friend this evening, Billy wondered if he believed all the hocus-pocus himself.

"What must I do?" he asked the creature. "I wanna see that Tyrannosaurus come to life, just like Godzilla on TV!"

"Godzilla!" screamed Venkman as he burst into Egon Spengler's laboratory. "This thing looked like Godzilla, Egon! If Ray hadn't blasted it into the ghost-trap, I think it would'a eaten me!"

Egon hardly raised his eyebrows at his friend's description of their latest spectral adversary. "Yes, indeed," he mumbled, intent on the machinery in front of him. "This little device should prevent any one of us from undergoing the uncomfortable sensation of being eaten by an ectoplasmic entity."

"Sure," grinned Venkman. "What does it do?" Egon straightened, his face serious. Venkman recognised the look. It was time for a scientific explanation.

"Many of our enemies are simply ectoplasmic projections from a psychic/spiritual world," said Egon, in his best teacher's voice. "Recently though, I have realised that they don't always come from the same world! This device...", he allowed himself a rare smile, "...this device measures energy sources from an elemental dimension! That is, if you like, ghosts of things from the far reaches of Earth's past, things we may not even know anything about yet!"

Venkman snorted "Aw, c'mon, Egon, is it gonna rid us of our little friend Slimer? I mean, did you see the state of my uniform after that ectoplasmic eating-machine got his hands on it?"

He paused as he noticed the solemn look on Egon Spengler's face. "Peter, we never know *what* we may have to face. You should know that by now. *We never know.*"

Billy stared up through the darkness at the massive skeleton of the Tyrannosaurus, the small red-eyed creature perched on his shoulder like a manic parrot.

With its help, Billy had slipped easily past the night-watchman. They'd got in through a tiny side window near the museum's North exit. It had been open, just as the creature had said. "Now take your stick of chalk," it rattled, "and draw the mystic circle around these old bones, just as the spellbook says".

Already, in his mind's eye, Billy could see the mighty Tyrannosaurus in all it's primeval glory thundering through the concrete jungle, escaping from man's world into far-off deserts.

"When will the Tyrannosaurus be here?" he asked the red-eyed creature.

With a leathery flapping sound, the thing launched itself from Billy's shoulder to land atop the dead skull of the Tyrannosaurus. "Soon . . ." it rasped softly, "Soon . . . begin the ritual!" Billy began to chant the strange spell from his aunt's dusty old book as he drew a chalk circle around the base of the dinosaur's skeleton. *"Garathrax spethod pax saurian mortis requidh!"*

"SOON!" snickered the creature, its wings shaking with evil mirth. "Soon...!"

Egon switched on his new machine and, to his surprise, the reading went off the scale. "Peter!" he cried to the bored Venkman. "Look at this! Quickly!" Venkman watched the needle registering Egon's new-found, other-dimensional energy. "Ahh, that's just a power surge," he laughed. "You've only just turned it on". To Egon's disappointment, Peter Venkman appeared to be right. The needle gradually fell back to zero and stayed there. Egon muttered crossly to himself, "I wish I could be sure..."

As Billy stopped chanting, the air in the dinosaur room became very still and cold. The red-eyed creature vanished, and Billy began to wonder if he wasn't still back home in bed, dreaming. Then there was a dull rumbling noise, almost beyond the range of human hearing. The ancient bones of the Tyrannosaurus seemed to be lit from within with an unearthly glow and a freezing wind suddenly swept through the whole building. Billy had to anchor himself to one of the ceiling pillars to stop himself being blown away, and he had to stop himself from crying out with a mixture of joy and horror...

Before him, the King of the Dinosaurs was coming to life. The bones became white and new and then wrapped themselves up in tendon and muscle. Blood vessels traced their way over the new flesh like a super-animated red wire before being enclosed by more layers of fat and muscle. Folds of reptilian skin grew taut as the wind stopped rustling and Billy gasped as two great baleful eyes flicked open and fixed him with a mesmeric stare.

The Tyrannosaurus shook his great head slowly and spoke in a voice that he not only heard but felt in the back of his skull. "FOOOOOD!" Billy gulped and for the first time wondered if he'd made a mistake. It was then he heard the stifled cry of the night-watchman, who had just appeared at the entrance of the Early Mammals gallery. Terrified beyond all reason, old Joe Crow could only stand in horror as the dinosaur spun around to face him. The Tyrannosaurus' jaws seemed to break into a huge grin that revealed a line of six-inch jagged teeth, then it turned its huge head towards Billy bellowing out "FOOOOOD!" once again. With that, old Joe was off like a rocket. He had just made it to the phone up in his office, when he heard the main doors groaning as the dinosaur sought to be free. The sound was followed by that of falling rubble. He dialled for emergency services and spoke calmly to the nice lady at the police station: "Excuse me," he said, "but there's a Tyrannosaurus Rex loose on Central Park West!"

Billy's Aunt Lavinia started in disbelief when she found the centuries-old book of spells tossed carelessly aside in her library. Horror-stricken, her instincts led her to the most dangerous spell in the book: page 4043, the call for the ancient Pagan Beast... Frantically, she scrabbled for the phone.

Billy was worried. The Tyrannosaurus looked great, sure enough, but it wouldn't head in the direction Billy wanted it to. It had already trashed two apartment buildings, excavated a subway station and stamped on a Baskin-Robbins ice-cream store. Now it was headed for midtown Manhattan, and Billy suddenly wanted to know what it would do when it got there...

Egon tapped his new device once more. "Peter, it's registering energy again, we really must look into this."

"Ssssh", snapped Venkman, impatiently. "Will you take a look at *this*?"

Egon saw that Venkman and his other two colleagues in spectre-splattering, Ray Stantz and Winston Zeddmore, were gathered around a flickering TV set. They appeared to be watching an old Godzilla movie.

Venkman scoffed, "Our business doesn't handle dinosaurs. Wouldn't it be better for them to call the Zoo?"

"I don't think so, Peter," said Egon. "This is hot. The PKE meter goes right off the scale."

As the four friends zoomed down their fire pole to ECTO-1, the Ghostbusters' receptionist, Janine, intercepted Venkman with a phone call. "It's a loony lady who says her nephew has raised a dinosaur from the dead. You wanna speak to her?" Venkman grabbed the phone and heard Billy's Aunt Lavinia ranting and raving on the other end. "Young man," she snapped when Venkman assured her all would be right in Manhattan within the hour, "you have no idea of what you are dealing with here. Your silly scientific contraptions will

never hold an ancient pagan force like this!"

"Don't worry Ma'am, it's all under control," cried Venkman, and slammed the phone down. ECTO-1's siren wailed and the Real Ghostbusters were on their way to face a new supernatural menace...

As ECTO-1 – which was, in fact, a converted ambulance – neared Central Park at the corner of Madison, Zeddmore was the first to notice the desolation of the streets, "Not a soul in sight," he murmured. "Now this just *ain't* New York City!"

With a thunderous roar, the creature stepped from behind the General Motors building. Venkman swerved ECTO-1 and narrowly saved the Ghostbusters from being stomped to death by a huge, reptilian foot.

With astounding professionalism, the 'Busters did the only thing they could do – scatter!

Breathing hard, Venkman and Egon sheltered behind the wrecked shell of a yellow cab. "Egon," Venkman panted, as he gazed up

at the roaming, spectral, dinosaur, "You plant the ghost trap in its path and I'll blast it with the –"

"Wait, Peter," shouted Spengler over the dinosaur's insistent roars, "This is no *ordinary* ghost. Wait..." But Venkman darted off to follow his plan, and gave Egon no choice but to follow his lead. As the dinosaur crashed through the wreckage it had caused, Egon noted that the deserted cityscape looked like some strange scene from the Tyrannosaurus' own era. The up-turned shells of burning cars submitted before the great reptilian king; the skyscrapers crumbled down and tumbled before his gargantuan blows. Egon dashed across the Tyrannosaurus' path and dropped the ghost trap in the middle of the road. He heard the sizzling sound of the proton beams from Venkman, Zeddmore and Stantz's guns joining in. He heard the roar from the beast and knew what had happened when he heard an odd crunching sound from the ghost trap. With a triumphant roar, the Tyrannosaurus Rex

turned and with one almighty flick of its tail revealed Venkman's hiding place behind an upturned hot dog stand. "Uh... Hi!" Venkman looked from side to side for a handy escape route and spotted the entrance to a subway station.

Venkman stood, apparently transfixed by the mighty dinosaur's gaze, "Uh... guys! this may take a little longer than we thought!" He suddenly catapulted himself sideways as the jaws of the beast snapped closed – splattering him with ectoplasmic saliva. He scrambled down the steps of the subway, but could still smell the breath of the dinosaur behind him.

Egon, Zeddmore and Stantz followed Venkman down into the subway, and the three reconvened on the D-train platform several levels below ground. "Okay, smart guy," growled Venkman at Egon, "what do we do?" Egon spread his hands as a sign of resignation, "I don't know, Peter, as I told you before, this is not a phenomenon of the type we have faced before. Although it is obvious that the force

The Ghostbusters, led by Billy's Aunt Lavinia, headed towards the sound.

It was late in the night when Peter Venkman paused among the trees of Central Park and glanced down at his PKE meter. He gulped – psychic energy levels were very high. The Tyrannosaurus was only yards away. Adjusting his spectro-visor, he peered into the dark. "Nothing." thought Venkman. "Good." He lifted the walkie-talkie that was strapped to the lapel of his slime-covered uniform and whispered as quietly as possible, "Egon? This is Peter. The thing is here, but I don't see it. Egon Spengler's voice boomed from the radio's speaker. "Okay Peter, stay..." Venkman's hand shot up to smother the speaker, and he glanced quickly in every direction. All was still, and he finally summoned up the courage to speak again. "Thanks, Egon, why don't you just put up a big sign saying 'Peter Venkman is *here*?'"

"Sorry, Peter," crackled Egon Spengler's voice, "but after all, that's what you're there for..." "Yeah..." said Venkman. "But to tell you the truth, I'm starting to get a little tired of being a dinosaur decoy".

"I know Peter, but just keep at it. Egon out."

Thanks a lot buddy, thought Venkman. He sighed, "Oh well, better get it over and done with!" He looked down at the PKE meter again, then stepped from the shelter of the trees and began walking across an open moonlit glade. The silence was near absolute, save for the distant roar of traffic and the occasional scream of a police siren. Venkman felt terribly exposed away from the comforting trees and was about to move back under the security of their leafy canopies when he registered movement out of the corner of his eye. He whirled, bringing up his proton cannon at the same time. Nothing! The PKE was going haywire. A twig snapped behind him, the noise deafening in the silence, and Venkman spun around again, but saw nothing in the deep shadows but darkness. The skin on the back of his neck crawled, and the hairs on

motivating this dinosaur is probably from another dimension, it does have corporeal existence. You came very close to being eaten."

"Yeah," fumed Venkman, "Look at the mess it made of my uniform!"

"Precisely," said a voice Venkman didn't recognise, "and that is why you should have listened to *me*!" The four friends turned and saw an outlandish figure standing a little way up the platform.

"Lavinia Von Erdeem..." she stated grandly, extending her hand to Egon, "...and *you*, sir, are a perceptive man." She turned to Venkman. "But you, are a *hothead*!" Venkman realised he was being addressed by the woman with the kooky voice whom he had hung up on an hour earlier.

Billy's Aunt Lavinia tapped Venkman squarely on the chest."You are dealing, not with a dinosaur, but with the resurrection of an ancient pagan force, banished long ago by Mother Nature. It is tarnishing the good name of dinosaurs and you, sir..." she tapped Venkman again, "...are letting it get away with it." For once, Venkman was speech-

less. Egon listened carefully as Aunt Lavinia told them how she suspected her young nephew was responsible for the dinosaur's resurrection, and how she suspected that there was very probably another evil creature involved, aside from the Tyrannosaur itself.

"So how can we send it back?" asked Stantz. Lavinia surveyed the foursome before her and clicked her tongue. "Ghostbusters, eh? Despite all your technology, you cannot overcome this beast. We must return to tried and trusted methods: we shall return this force from where it came by the same method it came here: by creating an inter-dimensional portal!!!"

"A portal?" said Venkman. "No time for explanations!" barked Aunt Lavinia as she turned and led the Ghostbusters back to the street above.

The Dinosaur's trail was not hard to follow. It had left a very obvious wake of destruction that led straight into Central Park. In the unnatural silence that enveloped midtown Manhattan, a distant crashing of trees could be heard.

his arms stood up as fear gripped him like a vice. Then the darkness moved. Dark and malevolent, the phantasmic Tyrannosaurus exploded out of the trees bellowing "FOOOOOD!" as it did so.

"Whatever you say, pal", yelled Venkman, then wheeled about and ran like the wind…

Not for the first time, Peter Venkman felt fear well up in his soul. It was dry and numb, it gripped his heart and drained his legs of strength. The ground quaked beneath him as the dinosaur thundered in pursuit, and Venkman felt as if he was running agonisingly slowly. Where was the circle? He had lost all sense of direction. Was it ahead of him? Was it behind him? To the side?

Everyone looked up when Ray Stantz yelled "Here they come!" Spengler turned to see a terrified Venkman being chased by the monstrous Tyrannosaurus, and then looked back at the old lady and young boy standing at his side. "You know what you must do," said Lavinia, "Your friend must lead the elemental into the mystic circle. There its powers should be weakened sufficiently for your technology to hold it until I can close the circle. Then the dimensions will open and the phantasm will be hurled back into its own evil haven. But remember, your friend *must* be out of the circle or he may follow it!"

Egon nodded, then turned to Stantz and Zeddmore, "Get across to the other side of the circle. As soon as the Tyrannosaurus is in, let out a containment stream. Seconds later, the Ghostbusters were in position, Venkman entered the circle Lavinia had scratched in the grass but, sweating and exhausted, stumbled. Sensing victory, the Tyrannosaurus lunged forward for the kill, jaws agape, eyes bright. Billy looked on horrified, but his fearful cry was drowned out by the dinosaur's booming roar. It was in the circle now. Egon yelled into his walkie-talkie: "Let him have it!" Three incredibly bright streams of light smoked out of the trees around the circle, enfolding the Tyrannosaurus in a lattice-work of proton energy. The demon that

had misled Billy appeared on the beast's back and fought to break free of its bonds but found, to its horror, that their hold remained firm. It thrashed madly in its efforts to escape, and the Tyrannosaurus' roars reached ear-splitting proportions. Egon yelled into his radio: "Venkman, get out of the circle, we can't wait much longer!" Zeddmore's voice cut in: "Egon, my cannon's on meltdown!" Egon looked across to Venkman, who, still exhausted, was crawling on all fours away from the Tyrannosaurus towards the edge of the mystic circle. "Stay at it, Winston, just a few more seconds…"

"C'mon, Peter, C'mon!" Egon yelled. Venkman at last found the energy to stagger clear of Lavinia's circle, just as Zeddmore's proton beams failed. They had only seconds before the Tyrannosaurus

broke free, but the old lady appeared out of nowhere, gouged the last segment of the circle into the ground, and then stepped back and began her mystic chant. Moments passed and Ray Stantz's voice cried out, "This is *not* gonna work!" Then, in an instant, the dinosaur was consumed by a blinding white ball of witch light, and, before the amazed eyes of the Ghostbusters and young Billy, the Tyrannosaurus began to decompose. It's skin cracked and began to flake off in great chunks. Muscles and tendons shrivelled and new bones crystallised into fossilised stone. Finally, the skeleton collapsed, the massive skull coming to rest amid a tangled heap of ribs and vertebrae. In its eye sockets a bright red light flickered, dulled and then finally disappeared. The little demon that had brought the great

dinosaur to life struggled, trapped beneath a huge thigh bone. Slowly its efforts became weaker and weaker until with a 'Phut', and a whisp of vapour, it vanished back into its own dimension…

The Real Ghostbusters, Billy and his Aunt Lavinia stood in the Dinosaur Hall of the Natural History Museum on Central Park West. The skeleton of the Tyraonnosaurus had been collected from the Park and reassembled in its former resting place as the centrepiece of the 'Cretaceous Era' gallery. Billy gazed up at it in rapt admiration. "Ghostbusters," said Aunt Lavinia, "I cannot thank you enough for the great service you have done for the city of New York!"

Venkman grinned inwardly at Egon as he stepped forward and gave Lavinia a little bow. "We must thank you too," he said, "if it were not for your knowledge of what we were dealing with, we would never have defeated it."

"It was because of her knowledge that it got loose in the first place!" muttered Venkman under his breath.

"Er… it would help us if you would keep your spellbooks out of young Billy's reach until he's a little more responsible," volunteered Stantz diplomatically. Aunt Lavinia smiled knowingly, "Don't worry," she patted the boy on the head, "I put it all down to youthful zeal."

"I know what I did wasn't too clever," said Billy. "But didn't the Tyrannosaurus look cool when he was chewing on that downtown bus?" The Real Ghostbusters groaned collectively, but it quickly turned into a laugh. Billy gestured at the bones of a Triceratops standing a little way down the hall, "Wouldn't it be even *cooler* to see a couple of *those* guys battling it out on a primeval plain?"

The laughing stopped. Billy was clipped round the ear by his Aunt and quickly steered away from the dinosaurs' skeletons.

Venkman clapped his hand over his face in relief.

The others chuckled quietly and the four heroes, tired but victorious, turned and followed Billy and his aunt – leaving the dusty skeletons to their silent vigil for the night.

RAY STANTZ

Ray Stantz is just a big kid at heart. He has all the wild enthusiasm and exuberance of youth, coupled with an encyclopaedic knowledge of Weird Things that have happened throughout history. When others would, quite understandably, run in the face of supernatural danger, Ray will always stand wide-eyed before it, proclaiming the scientific importance of the event. Ray is also the most mechanically minded member of the group, fixing up Proton Packs, PKE Meters and any other odd devices that Egon may dream up. In the body Ghostbuster, Ray would be the hands.

THE REAL GHOSTBUSTERS™

Story **IAN RIMMER** ⊘ Art **PHIL GASCOINE** and **DAVE HINE** ⊘ Lettering **GORDON ROBSON** ⊘ Colouring **STUART PLACE**

38

THE RETURN OF MR STAY PUFT!

(SORT OF)

Story **JOHN FREEMAN** ⊘ Art **MIKE COLLINS** and **LEW STRINGER** ⊘ Colouring **LOUISE CASSELL**

It was a bright but cold day in London when the odd things started to happen. At first, it was just clocks moving backwards in Underground stations and parking meters throwing coins out of their slots. But, as the day drew on, the delays on the tubes could no longer be explained as the usual ones, and the absence of pigeons in Trafalgar Square filled everyone who passed through it with a strange feeling of unease. The bright sunshine gave way to a sudden dark that couldn't be put down to a typical winter's day because it was the tail-end of summer; the flashes in the sky could have been lightning, but what about the reports of green balls of light in Hyde Park, and mysterious shapes moving in the murky waters of the Thames?

As children hurried home from school in the increasing gloom, and people in offices thought about making their last cup of tea before calling it a day, strange sights you could only see from the corner of your eye started to unsettle even the bravest souls. Newspapers suddenly blew everywhere as bitingly cold air blew up from the Underground. Some said that they had seen some Thing blowing them from the stands. In offices, windows rattled – stopped – and then blew in, shattered glass seeming to fly everywhere. As people screamed in horror, the windows were suddenly back in place, and mocking laughter drifted across London in the growing wind.

The worst of the thing was that no-one could explain it. By the time the last editions of the evening papers were out, the reports of paranormal activity became even more bizarre and the city's population got nervous, then frightened. Some got so frightened that they made for home early, even the braver ones, wanting to get out of London and into the safety of out-of-town homes as fast as possible. They faced the usual problems of crowded tubes and busy buses in silence, anything to get OUT of the Capital. The wind got stronger, and fear increased, as if people's own worst fears were being sucked out of them and becoming real: people afraid of closed spaces started screaming to be let out of the rooms they were trapped in – except they were standing in the middle of rapidly emptying streets. Instead of taking their dogs for their evening walks, owners hid from them in their bedrooms and refused to come out.

"I don't understand what's happening," said the Prime Minister, turning an elegant

silver pen over and over in her hand as she read, and listened to, more and more alarming reports of terrified people around the city. Despite the bright lights of the Cabinet Meeting Room, the shadows in its corners seemed blacker than usual as she glanced around at her worried ministers.

"Are we under attack? Is this some sort of chemical warfare?"

"The scientists don't seem to think so," the Defence Minister replied. He looked nervously around the room.. "They think," he added gravely, "that this might be some... supernatural force."

"Minister, I did not call this Emergency Meeting of Cabinet to listen to the somewhat fanciful explanations of so-called scientists. There must be a more rational explanation for this..."

"We do have some evidence to support this theory, Ma'am," the Defence Minister added hastily, passing photographs and electronic graph sheets around the table. "There's been a large increase in electromagnetic energy in the London area. This has been known to have an effect on both animal and human behaviour. Then there are the sightings of – ghosts – in the streets."

"I see." The Prime Minister sat in silence for a few seconds. A sudden wind howled outside. "There must be something we can do about this, someone we can call..."

"Ghostbusters, Ma'am?"

The ministers turned to look sneeringly at the Junior Secretary for Foreign Affairs.

"Ghostbusters, Michael? Tell me more!"

"They're a private firm in New York, ma'am. They... ah...

catch ghosts. Ghost Busters, you see and..."

"Yes, I see." the Prime Minister cut in. Click click went the pen in her hand. The wind howled again with renewed menace. A couple of ministers turned their collars up. Suddenly, the Prime Minister reached for the telephone on the table in front of her and began to dial an international number. A piercing, mocking laugh cut through the room as she did so and the hair on the back of several necks stood up and cold shivers ran down spines as the last number was dialled. "I think there is some merit in the Junior Minister's suggestion, gentlemen, since it is nothing any of us have experienced – ah, hello operator, I would like you to put me through to Ghostbusters Headquarters, New York. No, I don't have the number! That's what YOU'RE THERE for!"

"So that's London," Peter Venkman drawled as the Executive jet the Ghostbusters were flying in turned over the capital and prepared for its descent to Heathrow airport. "Sure is foggy down there..."

"That'll be the Ectoplasmic Field I'm picking up on the monitors," Egon Spengler replied, not looking up from the number of weird and fragile instruments that were spread around him. "If you can see it, things must have got worse since the Prime Minister called."

"Is that what's causing all those people to see things? The Fear Field?" asked Ray Stantz, his face lighting up with interest. This time, Ray did look up.

"Ray, you read too many popular papers. This is a fascinating scientific puzzle –"

"Which just happens to be driving Londoners out of their minds," Venkman cut in.

"Which is why we're here, right?"

"Er, right."

"So all we have to do is find the centre of this field and discover what's causing it, right?" Winston posed the question then stared nervously out of the plane window. "Heck, I'm not sure I want to go into that thing if it does what we've been told. We might not come out!"

"Canyoueatit?" piped up the Ghostbusters' ectoplasmic friend, Slimer, who, as usual, was feeling hungry.

"Now there's an idea," Peter snarled. "How about I drop Slimer into that gunk and see if he can eat his way through it?"

"Yeeeeerp!"

"Slimer." said Egon, turning back to his instruments. "Come out of that suitcase. We have to go into the field, but if my calculations are correct, then the helicopter that's waiting for us at Heathrow will put us

down near the centre, and we can do our job with minimum contact with the Subconscious Aggraphobic Fear Inducement area."

"That's great," replied Peter, "but what if your calculations are wrong?"

"Then we have a long walk ahead of us..."

"Are you SURE that the Telecom Tower is near here? I can hardly see a thing, even with the Spectro-visors!"

"Pretty sure, Winston. My PKE meter is reading strongest in that direction." Egon motioned to part of the thick, green fog that was swirling around them. The meter clicked in agreement.

"I managed to get through to the government offices before we left Heathrow," said Ray, checking his Proton Gun for the seventh time in five minutes. "Seems that a Gas Board Emergency Repair Team were doing some work in this area just before the paranormal happenings started up. Perhaps they dug up something they weren't expecting."

"Never mind that," snapped Peter. "Where are the ghosts?

We haven't found any yet, I – uuuuuuargh!"

There was a thump, then silence. Ray, Winston and Egon moved forwards to where Peter had been. "Guys," piped up a voice from a hole in the ground, "I think I found something."

"This must be the Gas Board works!" Ray leapt down into the hole, knocking Peter down as he was struggling to get up. "Hey, there's some sort of chest down here..."

"Don't touch that!" Egon pointed at the PKE Meter, which was clicking violently.

"This may be what we've been looking for..."

"Nooooo! You shan't have it! It's mine!" Without warning, a huge, fast-moving shape swept into the hole, grabbed the chest and disappeared deeper into the fog. The PKE Meters nearly exploded in the Ghostbusters' hands. "Ghostee!" said Slimer. The Busters ignored their paranormal friend and raced after the creature. "Anyone get a good look at it?" puffed Egon.

"Could have been anything," said Ray. "I think it had big teeth." Winston nodded in agreement but in the fog no-one could see either him or Peter so it hardly mattered.

"It's gone into the Tower!" Peter waited for the rest of the team at the heavy entrance doors. "It's open," he added.

"Of course it's open, whatever that thing is WANTS us to go in after it." Egon started checking his ghost trap.

"What are you talking about, Spengler?"

"The creature – whatever it is – has been feeding off the fears of the Londoners and using them to generate this – ahem – 'Fear Field'. But the Field has worked too well – it's scared everyone out of the city so the creature has nothing to feed on."

"You mean – it's hungry?"

"Precisely. Look – the fog is thinner than it was a couple of minutes ago – the ghost must be losing strength. We are the only source of nourishment the creature has, so it doesn't want to scare us – yet..."

"Oh wonderful. Well, let's get on with it." Peter was the first to begin the climb up the stairs of the Tower.

He was taking no chances though; his Proton Gun was fully charged and ready for use. A good thing too, because they were only half-way up when a horde of vile looking horrors started screaming at them from above. Peter started blasting. "No!" shouted Egon above the crackle of energy beams. "They're not really there. You've got to empty your mind."

Peter switched off the gun. After a couple of moments the horrors gave a few final wails of anger then vanished as quickly as they had appeared. The Busters continued their climb unmolested, but the air got colder and colder as they neared the top of the Tower.

Just one flight of stairs from the top, the air started to swirl with a rainbow of colours and a low-pitched moan sprang up around them. "Sub-sonics," muttered Egon. "Set at a level to cause fear, no matter how hard we try to block it out. This ghost is clever – this may take a little longer than we thought..."

"Don't give up hope," smiled Peter, "We've faced worse than this."

"We have?" said Winston, surrounded by balls of coloured light. "When was that, exactly?"

"Try to think of nice things, anything that wouldn't scare you," Egon shouted above the growing moans. "But not you, Ray, I remember last time we asked you to do something like

that you instantly thought of..."

The Ghostbusters reached the top of the stairs and stared in horror at the sight in front of them"... Mr Stay-Puft the Marshmallow Man!" Peter finished.

There it was all right, a mountain of white, topped with a grinning face and a cute sailor's hat. But there was nothing cute about this ghostly monster. It had a look on its face that you would be more likely to see on a werewolf just before it started to eat you. Swirling lights surrounded its body and from a strange collar around its neck came a green, evil glow. "Welcome, human gnats!" The ghost had a voice like a knife being scratched against a plate. "Welcome to the place where you will die!"

"Well if you're going to kill us, at least tell us who you are, first!" Peter shouted at the ghost, which became suddenly puzzled.

"Have I been imprisoned so long that you pathetic creatures have forgotten the greatness of The Morrigan?"

"Certainly looks that way, doesn't it?" Peter replied, smirking.

"Know then that I once ruled the lands of Britain, long ago! My people lived in fear of my ways, but it helped them fight their enemies, because that fear gave them great strength! Through me, through the wars I brought about by my powers, I began to create a race that would have ruled the Earth forever!"

"Sounds wonderful. What went wrong?"

"Bah! The fools rose up against me, seeking an end to all the wars and death. Their Druids imprisoned me, but now I am free, free to begin again. I will have human slaves to create new wars, new ways of death! Perhaps I will not kill

you after all..."

The Morrigan moved with incredible speed and plucked Ray from the floor with a giant hand. "You will be the first in my new army, you will be mine body and soul!"

Ray struggled to break free. The Busters fired their Proton guns as one, playing over the body of the Morrigan Stay Puft Man with deadly accuracy and away from the hand that held Ray. But the creature just laughed, throwing his head back in evil glee at their failure to trap him.

"Something's keeping the Morrigan anchored in our world!" shouted Egon.

"You think it could be that glowing thing around the Stay-Puft's neck.?"

"Of course! Ray! TRY AND GRAB THE NECKLACE!"

The guns blasted again, this time at the neck of the creature. It wailed in anger, staggered and suddenly Ray had his arms free and grabbed for the glowing object. It came free quite easily and, with a howl, the Stay Puft Man exploded into a thousand white fragments and vanished. Ray fell to the floor with a terrible thump.

"Well, that's that," said

45

Winston, wiping marshmallow from his eyes, "guess all we have to worry about now is the dry-cleaning bill."

"We're not out of the woods yet," snapped a bedraggled Peter. "Look at Ray!"

The air was swirling about Ray as he slowly stood up, eyes glazed, and turned towards the rest of the Ghostbusters. Slowly, he rose from the ground until he was floating a few inches above it. Then he began to walk towards them all, but very slowly and with an unhappy expression on his face.

"The Morrigan is trying to take Ray over!" cried Egon. "Ray, you've got to fight it."

"Egon!" Winston exclaimed suddenly. "Don't you see? The Gas workers must have released the necklace from that chest. If we can return the necklace to the chest, maybe we can stop this monster for good!"

Egon nodded in agreement and turned to Ray, who had broken out in a cold sweat. "Ray! Do you know where the chest is? Can you read the Morrigan's mind?"

"Of course he cannot, worm," came the screeched reply. It looked as though the Morrigan had taken over Ray completely. "And now, with this human as my vessel, I have no need for you! The chest is where none of you will ever find it!"

"Sumbudeeeluukingforthis?" Slimer smiled his enormous toothy smile as he emerged through the floor, chest in hands. Peter gave a yell of triumph and grabbed it. "Ray! Put the necklace in the chest. In the chest. PLEASE!" The Morrigan gave a howl of anger through Ray, and the air shimmered around the Ghostbuster. There seemed to be a creature with a hideous face forming around him, waving a black spear. Then Ray suddenly raised the arm that was holding the necklace and the apparition vanished. The room filled with wailing wraiths as slowly, slowly, Ray moved his hand over the chest. Peter opened the lid and Ray screamed in pain and dropped the necklace in.

The lid snapped shut immediately and the wraiths, the marshmallow, the lights and the fog all vanished at the same time, in the blink of an eye. Somewhere behind a distant cloud, the sun looked as though it was going to rise.

"Here be the Torc of Morrigan 'read Egon slowly from the strange inscription on the front of the golden chest. "Open this not, or wars without end, death without end, will forever be your curse."

"Sounds to me like we've pulled off a big one," said Winston. "Ray, are you all right?"

I'm a bit groggy, but yes, I'm fine. Shaken, but not stirred."

"There's just one thing," muttered Peter. "If all the evidence of this Morrigan creature vanished when we closed the lid of the chest, how are we going to get the British government to pay us for the clean-up? Will they believe us?"

"We cud all ways oopen thee box again!" Slimer suggested, grinning. The Ghostbusters exchanged glances briefly and then chased their ectoplasmic friend all the way down Telecom Tower into the bright, warm sunlight outside.

WINSTON ZEDDMORE

One day, Winston Zeddmore showed up at the Ghostbusters' headquarters looking for a job. He soon became the vital fourth member of the team. Of the four, he is certainly the most sensible, the one with his feet set most firmly on solid ground. When the others might not see a practical solution to a problem, it's Winston who cuts through all the nonsense and gives his all to put an end to the danger. In many ways he is the warmest, most open member of the team, and though he does not have the scientific background that the others share, he makes up for it with his sense of bravery, determination and loyalty. In the body Ghostbuster, Winston would be the heart.

JANINE MELNITZ

Nothing ever upsets Janine. Although she frequently pours sarcasm over everything her ghostbusting employers say and do, she remains effortlessly efficient and constantly cheerful. She is more than just a secretary or receptionist, and she knows it – she is the one person at Ghostbuster HQ that keeps the business looking like a business. She looks after her employers at all times, sends them out on missions and deals with their eccentricities with all the deadly efficiency of one who knows that, in reality, it's the receptionists that rule the world. She has a crush on Egon, but isn't exactly happy about having to compete with fungus for attention. In the body Ghostbuster, Janine would be the central nervous system.

THE REAL GHOSTBUSTERS™

Story **DAN ABNETT** ⊘ Art **BRIAN WILLIAMSON** and **DAVE HARWOOD** ⊘ Lettering and Colouring **HELEN STONE**

What, Where, When and Why?

Once upon a time. . . there were three scientists working at the Weaver Hall University in New York on a very peculiar subject: the phenomena of the supernatural. The three men were Peter Venkman, Egon Spengler and Ray Stantz, and although they took their subject very seriously, they found that few others did. Eventually the University, losing patience with the apparent waste of money the 'pointless' department represented, decided to cancel their funding.

The three men quickly found themselves penniless and their expertise ignored. It was Venkman's idea really, to turn their talents to a commercial venture – catching ghosts and solving people's supernatural problems professionally.

They took a lease on a disused fire station in downtown Manhattan as a headquarters for their operations. The fire station was in a bad state of repair and Spengler and Venk-

man were at first doubtful, but Ray was so keen on the fireman's pole that they had to take it.

The fire station is divided into three floors: on the ground is the parking space for the Ghostbusters' transport, and the reception area where all the calls and requests for help come in; on the first floor is a lounge, dining room and kitchen area for the Ghostbusters to relax in when not on duty; on the second floor Egon's cluttered research and development laboratory and the dormatory-style bedroom where the Ghostbusters sleep.

Ray also acquired the Ghostbusters' transport – an old Cadillac ambulance that cost them their last $5000. It didn't work terribly well, but they fitted it to carry the equipment they would need, and gave it a name: ECTO-1, the Ectomobile.

So they went into business, wearing their, now-famous, overalls, carrying their powerful Proton Guns and their nuclear-charged

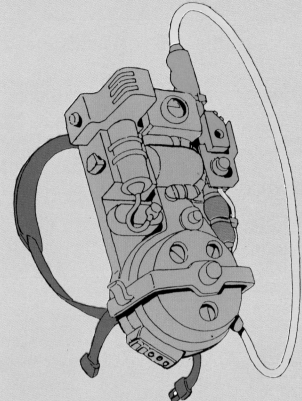

◄ backpacks, seeking out ghosts wherever and whenever they appeared.

Work was slow at first – few people believed that the Busters were serious and were reluctant to hire them. But out of desperation at the fall in custom he was suffering, the manager of the Sedgewick Hotel called the Ghostbusters to deal with a ravenous little ghost causing havoc on the twelfth floor.

This small, green, slimy spook (a class five, full-roaming vapour according to Ray) was difficult to catch. In busting it they broke tables, chairs, laundry trolleys, chandeliers and got themselves covered in slime from the high-speed, slop-eating, phantom. In the end they marched out of the devastated state ballroom with a full ghost trap and the satisfaction of knowing they had caught their first ghost.

Their reputation grew as the news of the bust spread. Suddenly everyone wanted the Ghostbusters to bust their ghost. The flood of business was handled by their invaluable receptionist, Janine Melnitz, but as the operation increased they found it necessary to employ another Ghostbuster. One day, Winston Zeddmore turned up at the HQ looking for a job. They appointed him on the spot.

WEAPONS

PROTON PACK – the Proton Pack is the basic Ghostbuster weapon. It consists of a portable nuclear accelerator and a particle thrower.

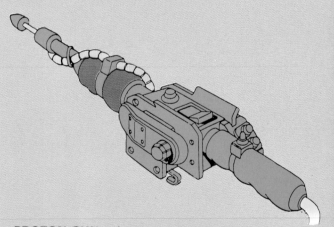

PROTON GUN – the Proton Gun is the actual shooting part of the Proton Pack. It fires a stream of high-energy ions that can be used to manoeuvre ghosts into the area above the ghost trap. The laser streams of two or more Proton Guns should never, ever, be crossed, or, as Egon warns, the result could be "very bad indeed."

GIZMOS & GADGETS

PKE METER – PKE stands for Psycho-Kinetic Energy. The PKE Meter is used by the Ghostbusters to detect the PKE left behind or generated by ghosts.

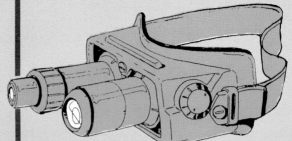

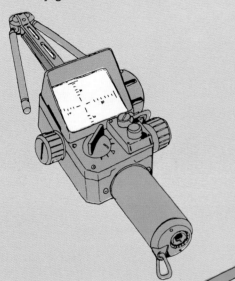

SPECTRO-VISOR – using the Spectro-visor, a Ghostbuster can see invisible ghosts and auras through the image-intensifying mechanism which operates on infra-red and ectoplasmic sensitive wavelengths.

GHOST TRAP – these are the shoebox-sized portable containment units used to temporarily enclose a ghost until the Ghostbusters can get it back to the main containment unit. The pedal at the end of the cable allows the Buster to spring the trap at a safe distance.

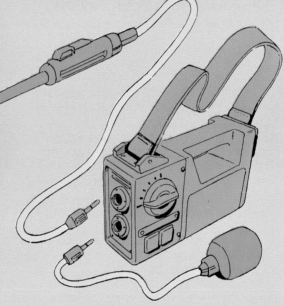

GHOST DETECTOR – also known as a 'sniffer', this samples air from a possibly haunted locale and analyses it for any free-floating ectoplasm.

The Ghostbusters faced their first great challenge in the early weeks of their career. Investigating the haunted fridge of a beautiful young woman called Dana Barrett, the Ghostbusters uncovered a dreadful supernatural conspiracy by the ancient demon Zuul to enter our dimension and bring about Doomsday. On the top of the Shandor Building, New York City, the four Ghostbusters stopped the progress of the demon, who had taken the form of a gigantic Mr. Stay-Puft Marshmallow Man, and proved their claim that they were here to save the world.

The final addition to the regular inhabitants of the Ghostbusters' HQ arrived shortly after this. During the battle with Zuul, the ecto-containment unit had been turned off and all the ghosts inside had been released, sending them on a terrible rampage around New York. Having dealt with Zuul, the Busters had to go and round them all up again.

One of the last ones to be recaptured was the small green spook from the Sedgewick Hotel that had been their first target. He had been joyfully eating his way through every burger stand and junkfood joint in the city. Egon decided to use him as an ectoplasmic guinea-pig in some of his experiments, because, unlike many other ghosts, he'd stay put (provided he was supplied with food!) and so he was never returned to the ecto-containment unit. Slimer, as he is now known, became a household 'pet' for the Ghostbusters, a ghost living with humans who could just about tolerate his more unpleasant habits. Sometimes, Slimer's appetite has clashed with Peter's, and Peter has threatened to zap him, but, like the other Busters, even Peter has a soft spot for the little green ghost. Ghostbusting is a tough, demanding, dirty, slimy job. So why do they do it? Peter Venkman: "I dunno, but busting makes you feel good!"

SLIMER

Long before Slimer left his first trail of ectoplasmic slime in kitchens and dining rooms around the world, he was an ordinary human being just like you and me. Well, not quite ordinary, he had a quite insatiable appetite and would greedily gobble away at any item of food that came his way, day or night. When he died, his soul refused to leave the mortal plane and so he has roamed the Earth in ectoplasmic form, happily eating anything he can get his stubby little hands on. He has completely forgotten his real name and so the Ghostbusters nicknamed him Slimer — due to his habit of, well, *sliming* people. He is undoubtedly a supernatural creature, but has sided with the good guys. He just wants to be loved and appreciated by people in general and Peter Venkman in particular. In the body Ghostbuster, Slimer would be the stomach.

SPOOKED OUT!

A GOTHIC MANSION IN UPSTATE NEW ENGLAND...

OKAY, GUYS, KEEP YOUR *PROTON GUNS* ARMED AND READY...

I THINK WE'VE FOUND THE LITTLE CREEPS!

SLURP!

GCK! GCK! GCK!

ZAP 'EM! THESE GHOSTS ARE *HISTORY*!

YOW! SCRAM! SCRAM!

RATS! THEY WERE TOO FAST FOR US!

LET'S SPLIT UP. *WINSTON*, TAKE THE KITCHEN. *RAY*, CHECK UPSTAIRS. *EGON*, COME WITH ME.

Story **JOHN FREEMAN** ⊖ Art **ANTHONY WILLIAMS** and **DAVE HARWOOD** ⊖ Lettering **ZED** ⊖ Colouring **HELEN STONE**

AND SO...

HA – A GHOST TRAIL IF EVER I SAW ONE.

UCK! HI THERE, SUNSHINE...

YIKES!

...CONSIDER YOURSELF *BUSTED!*

WAH!

MEANWHILE, IN THE LIBRARY...

COME TO DADDY, YOU TROUBLESOME SPOOK –

PETER! WATCH OUT FOR THOSE –

– BOOKS!

WHAT–?

WHUMP

TRY TO BE *CAREFUL,* PETER. THIS EQUIPMENT IS *EXPENSIVE!*

59